How to use this PAW Patrol Activity Book

This PAW Patrol Ready for School Activity Book has been written to help your child get ready for starting school. This book introduces numbers, shapes, colours and the alphabet, as well as encouraging children to think about their feelings, their daily routine and their likes and dislikes. With motivating activities that support the Early Years Foundation Stage, this book is perfect for children starting school and during reception year.

- Find a quiet, comfortable place to work.
- This book has been written in a logical order, so start at the first page and help your child to work their way through.
- Read out the instructions to your child where necessary and make sure that they know what to do.
- End each activity before your child gets tired in order to ensure that they will be keen to return to the activities next time.
- Help and encourage your child to check their own answers as they complete each activity. (Answers can be found on page 24.)
- Let your child return to their favourite pages after they have completed them. Talk about the activities they enjoyed and what they have learnt.
- Remember to give plenty of praise and encouragement.
- Once your child has completed all the activities in the book, reward them for their effort and achievement with the certificate on page 23.

Let the PAW Patrol help you get Ready for School!

PAW Patrol – here to help!

ACKNOWLEDGEMENTS

Published by Collins
An imprint of HarperCollinsPublishers Ltd
The News Building, 1 London Bridge Street, London SE1 9GF

HarperCollinsPublishers
Macken House, 39/40 Mayor Street Upper, Dublin 1 D01 C9W8, Ireland

© HarperCollinsPublishers Ltd 2023

10 9 8 7 6 5 4 3 2 1

ISBN 978-0-00-862002-8

British Library Cataloguing in Publication Data

A Catalogue record for this publication is available from the British library.

©2023 Spin Master Ltd. PAW PATROL and all related titles, logos, characters; and SPIN MASTER logo are trademarks of Spin Master Ltd. Used under license. Nickelodeon and all related titles and logos are trademarks of Viacom International Inc.

Consultant: Carole Asquith
Publisher: Jennifer Hall
Project editor: Katie Galloway
Cover design: Sarah Duxbury
Internal design: Ian Wrigley
Layout: Rose & Thorn Creative Services Ltd
Production: Emma Wood
Printed in Great Britain by Martins the Printers

Contents

All about me

Draw a picture of yourself. You might want to look in the mirror at the same time as you are drawing.

Draw a picture of the people you live with.

What do you like to eat? Circle the foods that you like.

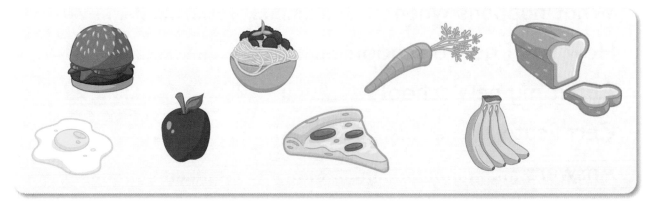

Where do you live? Write the name of your town.

Can you draw a picture of your home?

What do you like to do?
Circle the things that you like to do.

How to hold a pencil

Practise the snappy crocodile grip with a grown-up to help you.

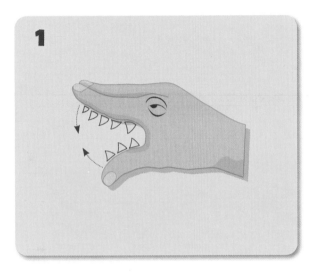

snap! snap! snap!

Make your hand into a snappy crocodile using your thumb as the bottom of the crocodile's jaw and your next two fingers as the top part of the jaw.

Your grown up helper will lay the pencil inside the crocodile's mouth. Now make the cheeky crocodile eat the pencil by snapping his mouth shut!

Let's draw patterns

Follow the dotted lines with your finger to help the pups get to their bowls. Then trace the dots with your pencil. Start at the red dot.

Let's learn numbers 1 to 5

The pups love to count! Count the paw prints under each number, then say the numbers out loud.

Now trace the dots with your pencil to write the numbers.

Draw lines to match the numbers to the pictures.

1
2
3
4
5

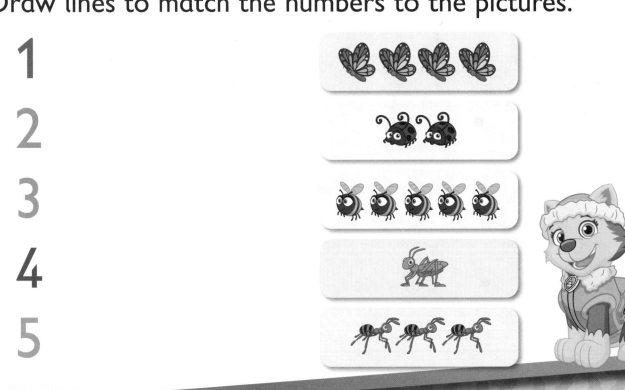

Let's learn numbers 6 to 10

Count the paw prints, then say the numbers out loud.

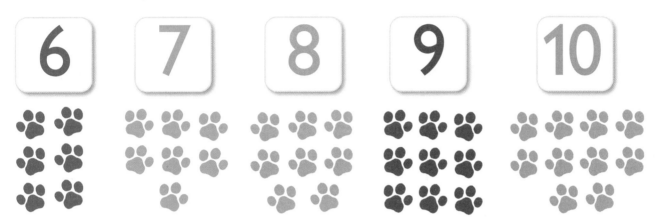

Now trace the dots with your pencil to write the numbers.

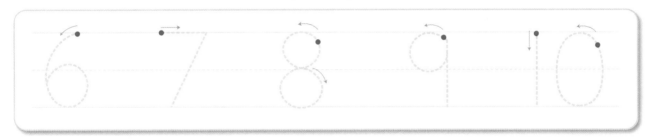

Count the number of treats in each box and then trace the number with your pencil.

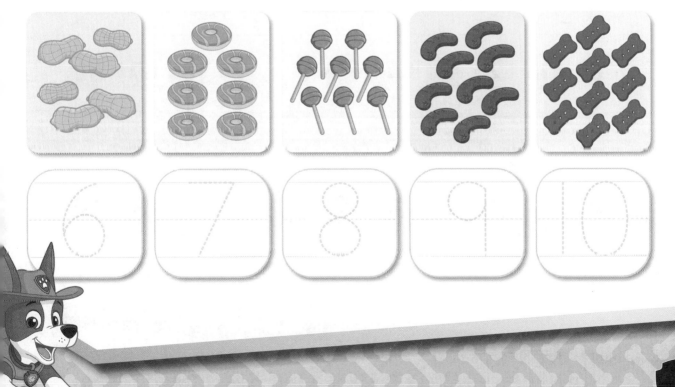

Number order 1 to 10

Rubble is making a number line. The number line shows the order in which the numbers 0 to 10 must go.

Fill in the missing numbers to help Rubble complete these number lines.

Chase is on the case! Join the dots in order from number **1** to number **10** to help Chase complete his picture.

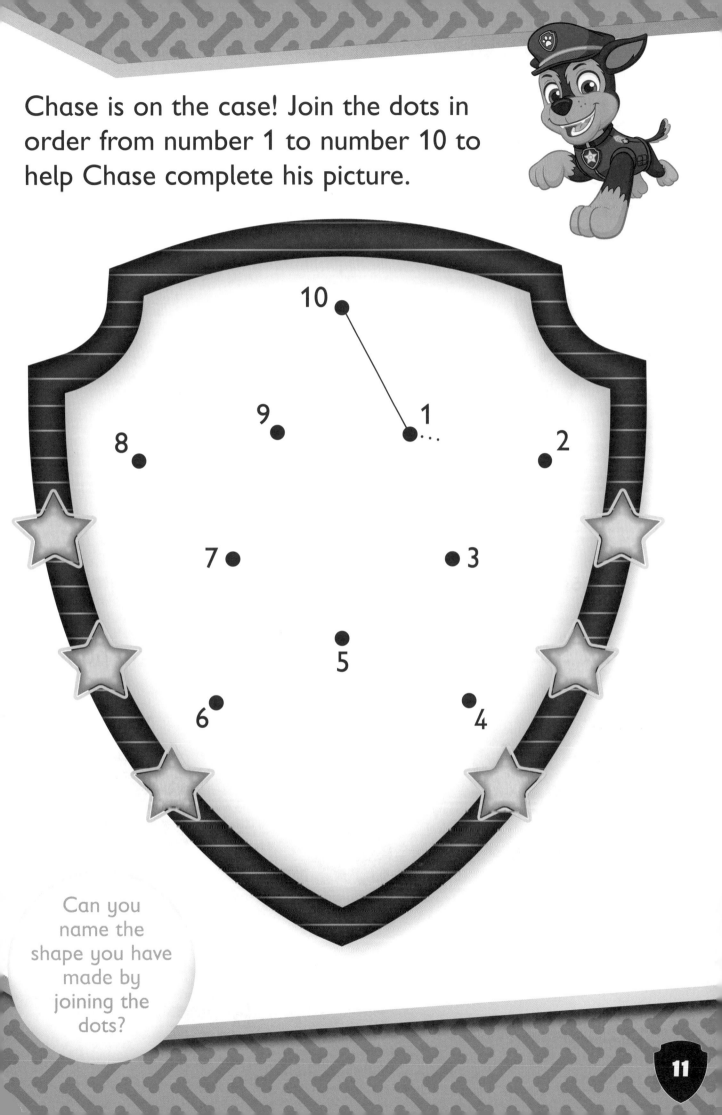

Can you name the shape you have made by joining the dots?

All about shapes

Start at the red dot then follow the arrow to trace each shape. Say the names of the shapes out loud.

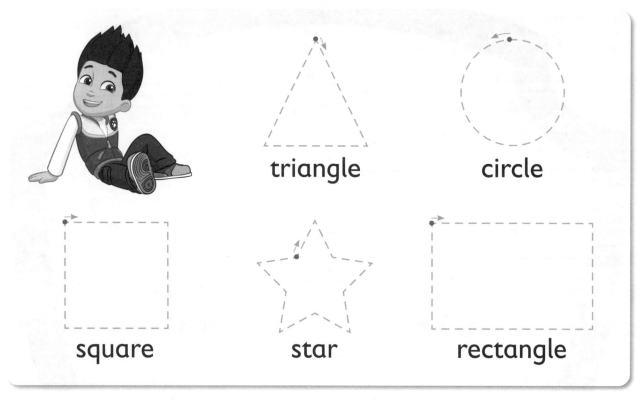

triangle

circle

square

star

rectangle

Draw oval shapes to make cosy beds for the pups.

Let's practise colours

Can you see your favourite colour?

The pups are sorting things into groups of the same colour. Circle the odd one out in each group.

Can you say the colour of the odd one out in each group?

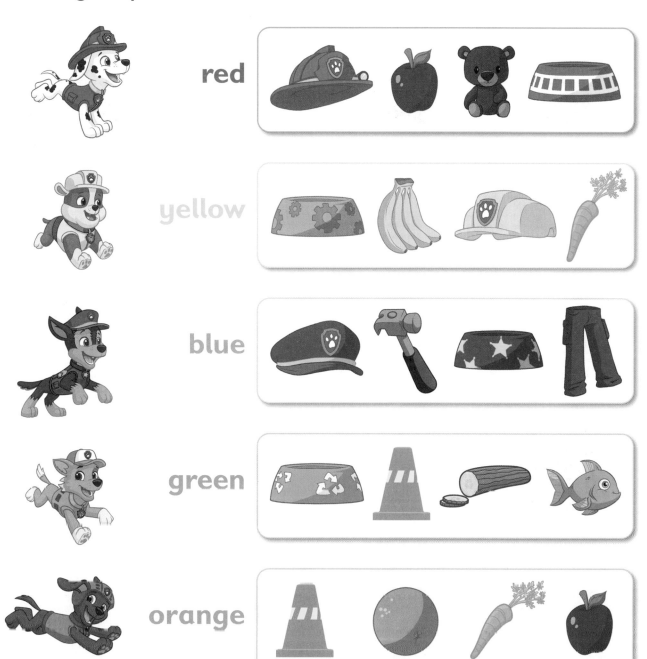

red

yellow

blue

green

orange

The alphabet

Here are the letters of the alphabet in order. Trace the letters and then say them out loud. For the letters that don't have a picture, try to find something on the page that begins with that letter. You could draw it in the box.

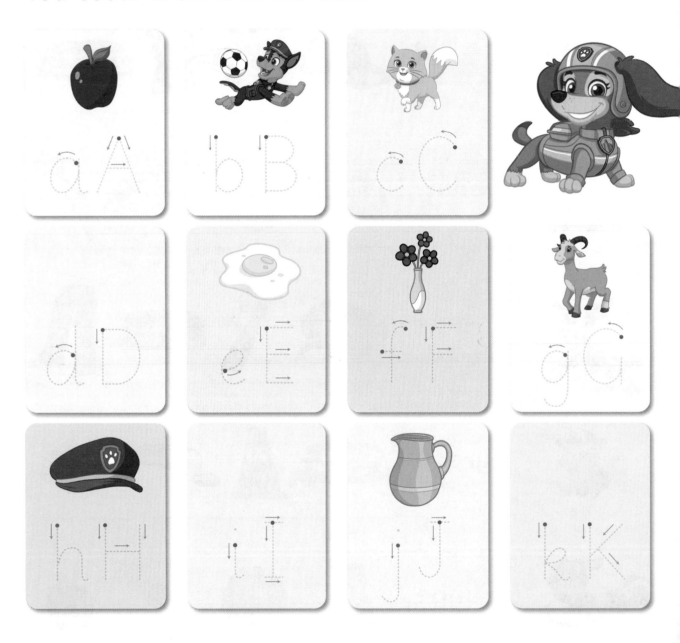

Names start with a capital letter.
Point to the letter that starts your name.
Now point to the other letters in your name.

Capital letters

Look at the pictures below. Trace the first letter of each pup's name using a capital letter.

 Chase

Marshall

 Rubble

Skye

 Tracker

Zuma

Alphabet order

Join the dots in order from **a** to **z** to finish the picture and find out what Rubble is dreaming about.

How are you feeling?

We can use words to say how we feel.

Look at the pictures of the pups. Circle the word that describes how each pup is feeling.

happy   scared   tired   happy

tired   sad

excited   happy   worried   proud

sad   sad

excited   cross   cross   surprised   tired   tired

How are you feeling today?

Tick the boxes to say how you are feeling.

happy	☐	sad	☐	tired	☐
excited	☐	surprised	☐	worried	☐
proud	☐	scared	☐	cross	☐

What happens when?

Ryder has a busy day ahead!

Can you sort these pictures into the order in which they happen? Write the numbers **1**, **2**, **3** and **4** into the boxes to put the pictures in order.

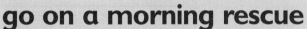

go on a morning rescue

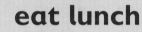

eat lunch

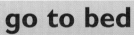

go to bed

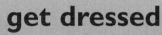

get dressed

How will I get to school?

The pups have different ways of getting to places.
Children have different ways of getting to school.
Circle how you will get to school.

walk

car

bus

train

bike

Trace the lines to help the pups get to the Lookout.

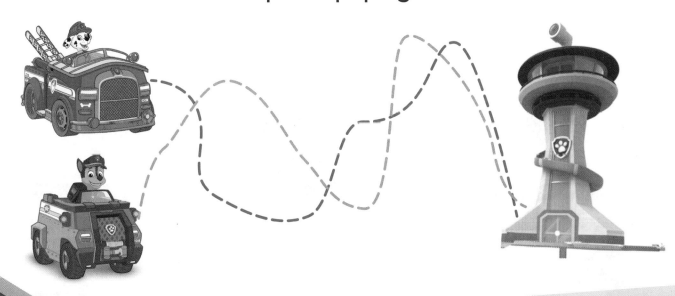

About my new school

Write down the name of your new school.

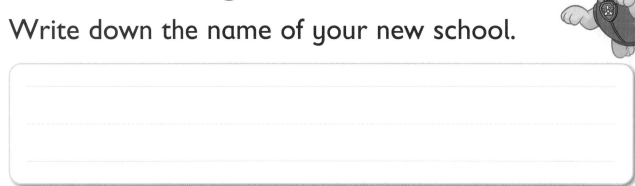

Can you draw a picture of your new school?

Here are some things you might do at school. Circle the things you would like to do.

This badge is awarded to

....

Age ....

For successfully completing

PAW Patrol
Ready for School
Activity Book

Date ....

Signed ....

Well done!

Answers

Page 4
Picture of child drawn
Picture of people lived with drawn
Foods child likes circled

Page 5
Name of town written
Picture of home drawn
Activities child likes circled

Page 7
Patterns traced correctly

Page 8
Paw prints counted and numbers said out loud

Numbers traced correctly

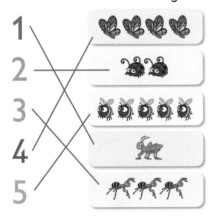

Page 9
Paw prints counted and numbers said out loud

Numbers traced correctly

Number of treats in each box counted correctly

Numbers traced correctly

Page 10
2, 9
1, 4
3, 6
7, 8

Page 11
Dots joined in order and picture completed

Page 12
Shapes traced correctly
Oval beds drawn

Page 13
red – teddy bear circled (brown)
yellow – carrot circled (orange)
blue – hammer circled (black)
green – traffic cone circled (orange)
orange – apple circled (red)

Page 14
Letters traced correctly
dD – deer
iI – igloo
kK – kite

Page 15
Letters traced correctly
tT – trousers
wW – walrus
zZ – zebra
Letters in child's name pointed out

Page 16
Capital letters traced correctly

Page 17
Dots joined in order and picture completed

Page 18
Skye – scared
Rubble – happy
Marshall – sad
Chase – proud

Page 19
Zuma – excited
Rocky – surprised
Boxes ticked to show child's feelings

Page 20

Page 21
Method of transport circled
Lines traced correctly

Page 22
Name of school written
Picture of school drawn
Activities child would like to do circled